D0240419

BOOK

THE TALKING BALL

CHIPPY CHAPLIN, the gipsy lad, was being chased for his life! But he had the strangest helper any runaway ever had. It was a great big Ball which carried him off, balancing him on top and bouncing him over every obstacle.

The Ball had not always been so big. But when Chippy let it out of a curious flask he found, it grew and grew—and what's more, it talked! A voice that seemed to come from it told Chippy it would lead him to his long-lost father.

So Chippy followed the Talking Ball. He ran away from his villainous Uncle Ezra—and here he was still on the run.

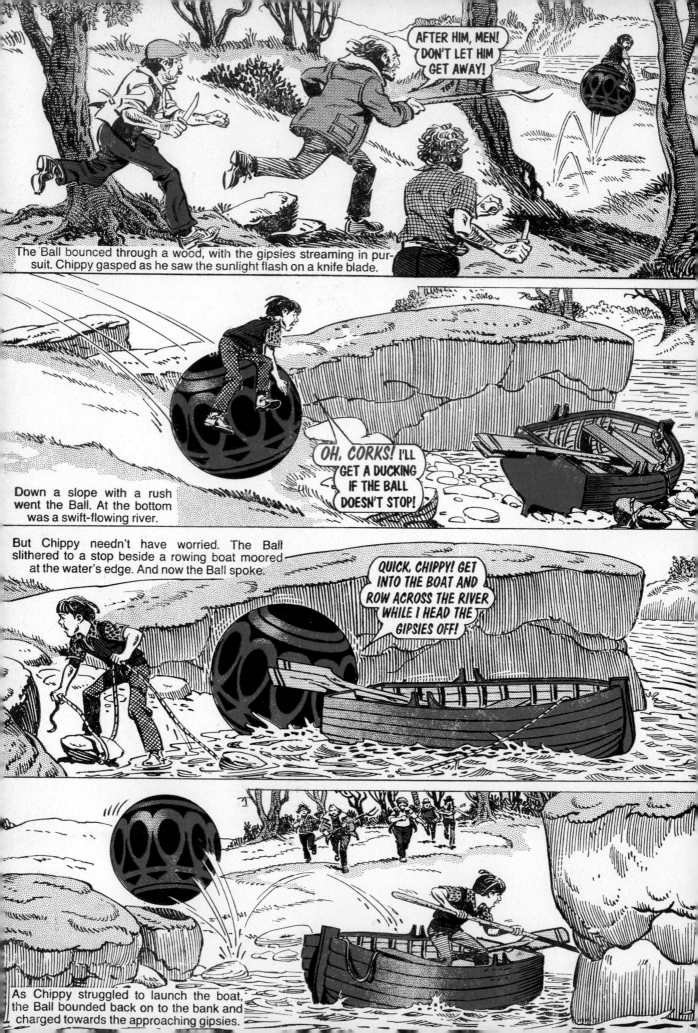

The Ball bounced through a wood, with the gipsies streaming in pursuit. Chippy gasped as he saw the sunlight flash on a knife blade.

AFTER HIM, MEN! DON'T LET HIM GET AWAY!

OH, CORKS! I'LL GET A DUCKING IF THE BALL DOESN'T STOP!

Down a slope with a rush went the Ball. At the bottom was a swift-flowing river.

But Chippy needn't have worried. The Ball slithered to a stop beside a rowing boat moored at the water's edge. And now the Ball spoke.

QUICK, CHIPPY! GET INTO THE BOAT AND ROW ACROSS THE RIVER WHILE I HEAD THE GIPSIES OFF!

As Chippy struggled to launch the boat, the Ball bounded back on to the bank and charged towards the approaching gipsies.

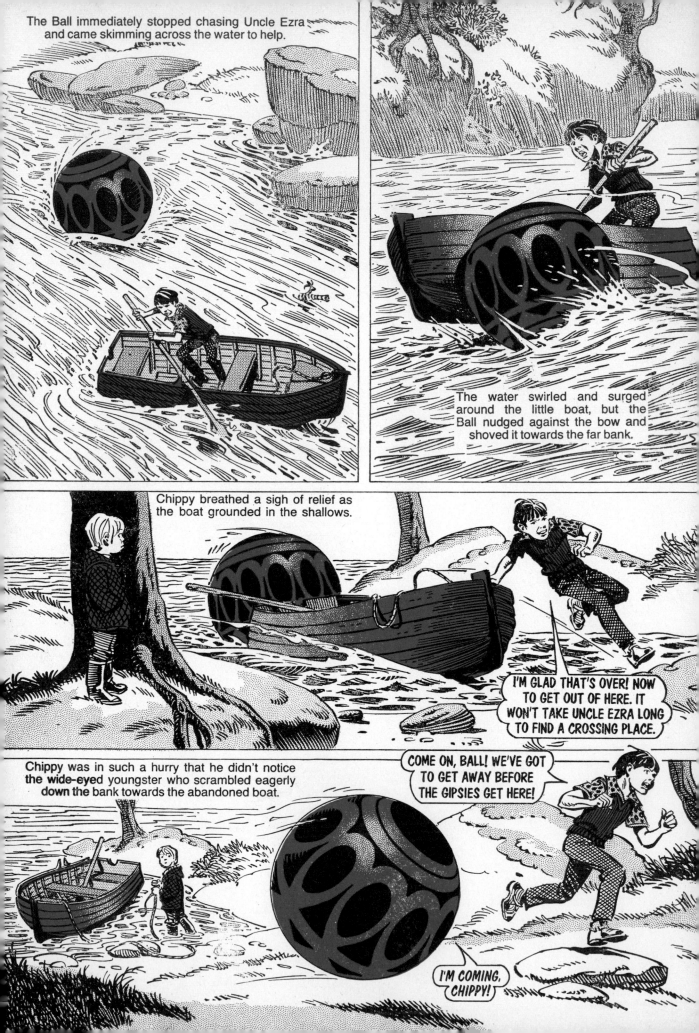

The Ball immediately stopped chasing Uncle Ezra and came skimming across the water to help.

The water swirled and surged around the little boat, but the Ball nudged against the bow and shoved it towards the far bank.

Chippy breathed a sigh of relief as the boat grounded in the shallows.

I'M GLAD THAT'S OVER! NOW TO GET OUT OF HERE. IT WON'T TAKE UNCLE EZRA LONG TO FIND A CROSSING PLACE.

Chippy was in such a hurry that he didn't notice the wide-eyed youngster who scrambled eagerly down the bank towards the abandoned boat.

COME ON, BALL! WE'VE GOT TO GET AWAY BEFORE THE GIPSIES GET HERE!

I'M COMING, CHIPPY!

The small boy screamed in terror as he and boat and Ball were hurled into space.

What did Uncle Ezra mean? Chippy soon found out. As the Ball drew nearer, his uncle pulled out a wicked-looking knife!

GOT IT!

At such close range the rogue couldn't miss. He yelled with glee as the knife-point drove in—and the Ball burst with a tremendous bang!

Uncle Ezra flung Chippy to the ground and dared him to move while they searched for the burst Ball. But his triumph turned sour, for it had disappeared! The gipsies combed the grass and the bushes, but there was no sign of it.

KEEP SEARCHING! IT MUST BE HERE SOMEWHERE!

Chippy was lying still, sunk in gloom. The Ball, he knew, would have shrunk to the size of a marble, but it would swell up again and his uncle would find it. Time passed —and then Chippy thought he felt the ground heave under him.

GOSH! IT MUST BE THE BALL! IT MUST HAVE ROLLED DOWN A RABBIT BURROW!

Chippy began to crawl away in case the Ball burst through there. But Uncle Ezra thought he was trying to escape.

WHAT ARE YOU UP TO, BOY? STAY WHERE YOU ARE!

The gipsy leader stepped towards Chippy—then got the fright of his life when the ground erupted under him and the Ball hurled him off his feet.

AAARGH!

THAT WILL TEACH HIM!

RUN FOR IT, CHIPPY!

THE BALL HASN'T GROWN TO ITS FULL SIZE YET. IT SHOULD BE ABLE TO MAKE ITS WAY THROUGH THE TREES NOW.

Chippy ran for it, and the Ball came bounding along after him.

The runaway put plenty of space between himself and the gipsies, but he needn't have hurried. Uncle Ezra had been knocked cold, and the other rogues weren't so keen to have a go at tackling the Ball on their own.

Chippy was beginning to feel hungry after his adventure. Where could he get something to eat? Suddenly the Ball flashed past him and into the river.

It disappeared under the surface and then whooshed up to flip a big fish on to the bank.

GOSH! GOOD OLD BALL! IT MUST BE A MIND READER!

Chippy's mouth watered as he lit a fire and cooked his fish. He was safe now, with his strange guardian back to its full size and able to protect him again.

It was a long time after this till the Ball tracked down Chippy's father. But father and son were united at last, and it was all thanks to the mysterious Talking Ball from that queer old gipsy flask.

GUESTS AT THE GREYTOWERS GARDEN PARTY...
THEN COMES MRS THISWUN AND HER STORY TELLING DAUGHTER, JUNO THISWUN.
AND MR NEEPOT AND HIS DIRTY SON, JIM NEEPOT.
MR OLD IRON AND HIS RUSTY-LOOKING SON, ERNIE OLD IRON.
FROM RUSSIA, COMRADE OFFALKOF AND HIS SHIVERING SON, IVAN OFFALKOF.
MRS SWEATHER AND HER SUN-TANNED DAUGHTER, GLORIA SWEATHER.
FROM SCOTLAND MR LUMMY AND HIS COO LUMMY (WHY ON EARTH DID HE BRING HIS COO?)
MR ATWITT AND HIS SILLY SON, WATT ATWITT.
AND LAST OF ALL MR MOBILE AND HIS SPEEDSTER SON, OTTO MOBILE.
HOOT!

DIRTY DICK

DESPERATE DAN

THERE ARE ALL YOUR APPLES, FARMER.

THANKS, D.D!

I'M OFF QUICK! DUST HAS GOT UP DAWG'S NOSE, AND I THINK HE'S GOING TO SNEEZE AGAIN!

AA-AH-AH!

CHOOOOOO!

BLOW

HEY! YOU'VE BLOWN AWAY MY PRIZE EXHIBIT!

GEE, SORRY! I'LL GO AND GET IT BACK!

WHATEVER IT WAS, IT WENT TOWARDS THE APPLE ORCHARD.

HO-HO! PICKING BONES OFF THE TREES IS MUCH TASTIER THAN PICKING APPLES!

SIR COWARD de CUSTARD

BAH! IT'S NOT FAIR! I HAVE TO WALK AND CARRY ALL THIS HEAVY GEAR. IT'S TIME I GOT A TURN RIDING THE HORSE!

OO-ER!

STAND AND DELIVER!

BUT I'M ONLY A PENNILESS KNIGHT. I HAVE NO VALUABLES.

HE HASN'T SEEN ME. I'LL NIP INTO THE BUSHES.

WELL, I'LL TAKE YOUR HORSE!

THIS WILL STOP THE VARLET!

OOF!

BOOM!

WAH! I'VE BEEN SHOT!

ERK!

HE BE DISARMED, SIRE! NOW'S YOUR CHANCE!

QUICK, SIRE! HERE COMES THE SHERIFF!

GROAN!

WELL DONE, BOY! I MIGHT HAVE GOT HURT TACKLING THE VILLAIN ON MY OWN!

TEE-HEE! SIR COWARD GOT A REWARD FOR CAPTURING THE VARLET. BUT I GOT A BETTER REWARD. HE BE TOO SORE TO SIT ON A SADDLE NOW!

CORPORAL CLOTT

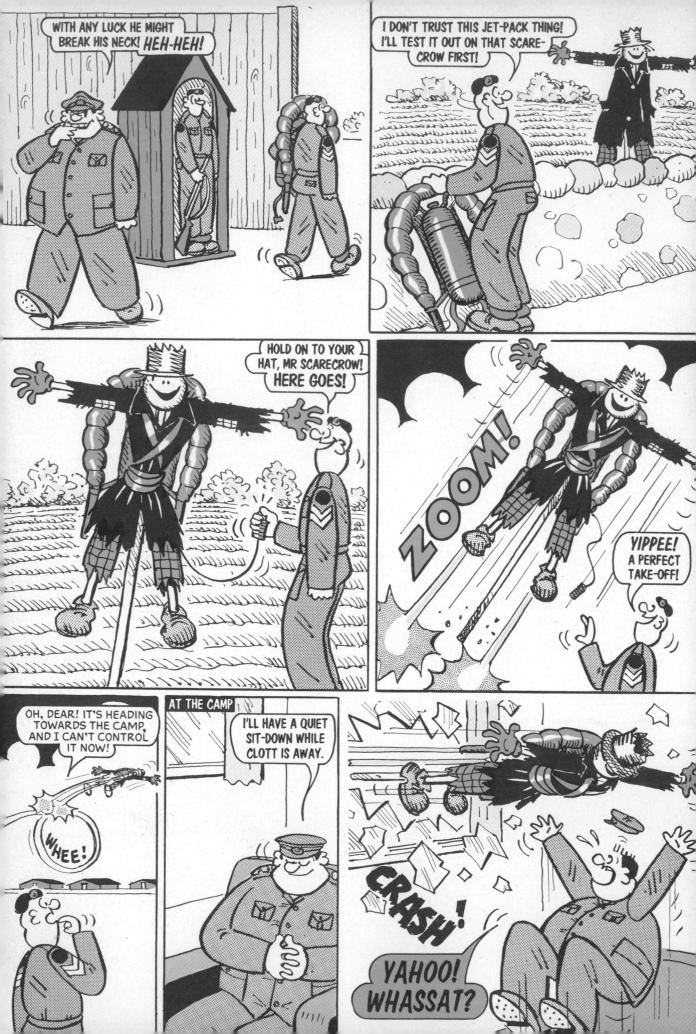

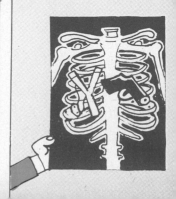

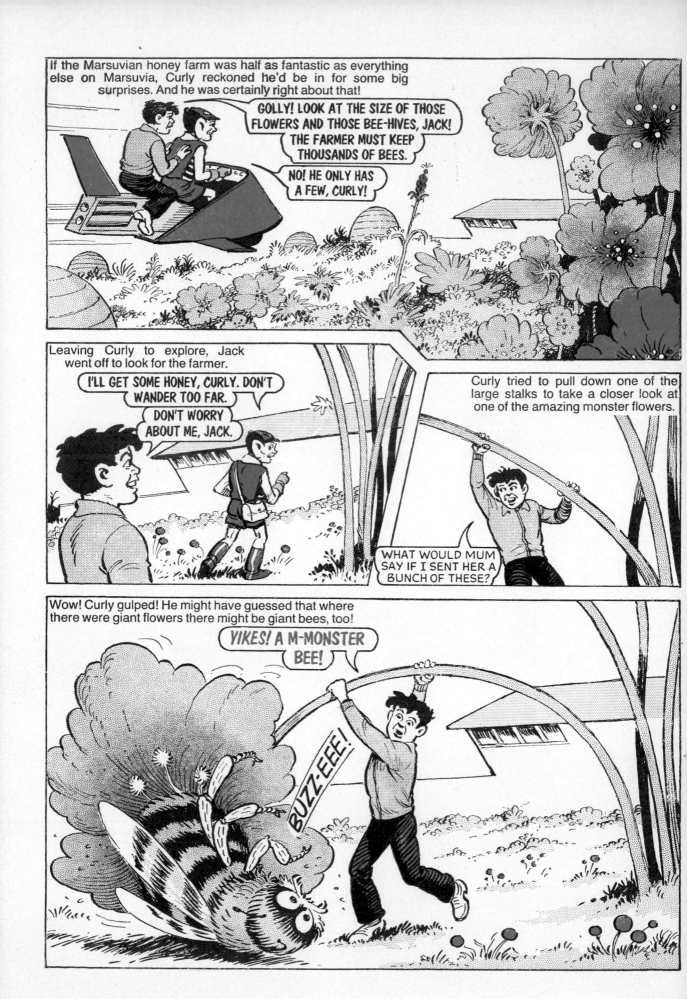

BUZZ-ZZZ-ZZ!

The giant bee buzzed angrily. Curly ran. There was nowhere to hide in this flowery glade. In desperation he leaped to seize hold of the sturdy-looking stamens of a bell-flower.

IF THAT BRUTE STINGS ME, I'M A GONER! HELP!

BUZZ-ZZZ!

GASP! I CAN HEAR IT COMING!

Pulling with all his weight, he dragged the flower down over his body to shield himself.

Whump! The diving bee alighted with such force that it crushed the flower downwards on Curly. And the stamens broke off in his hands.

BUZZ-UMP!

OOH! IT'S CRUSHING ME!

PEE-YOING-GG!

BUZZ-AAH!

GASP! WOULD YOU BELIEVE IT?

The result was surprising. For as the stamens broke, the flower sprang upright again and catapulted the bee into the air.

It seemed impossible, but Jack meant to give chase! And Curly gasped when his space chum explained how he planned to do it.

WE'LL RIDE ON THESE BUZZERS, CURLY. I USED TO HAVE GREAT FUN ON THEM BEFORE I GOT MY SCOOTER. THEY'RE A LOT FRIENDLIER THAN THEY LOOK, YOU KNOW!

YOU MUST HAVE STIRRED IT UP, CURLY. LOOK, THIS ONE'S HARMLESS!

WHAT! BUT THAT'S THE SORT OF BRUTE THAT ATTACKED ME!

BUZZ!

The giant bees were called Buzzers on Marsuvia and they were really tame if you didn't annoy them by knocking them off their flowers!

Curly stepped astride gingerly as Jack gave his mount a squeeze with his knees and rode it up into the air.

HURRY, CURLY!

GOLLY! FANCY ME RIDING A BEE!

The bees were fast. They began to overtake Jack's scooter, which was slowed down by the two men's weight.

SNARL! THOSE KIDS ARE ASKING FOR TROUBLE, NASTI. LET'S GIVE THEM SOME. LOOK, THERE'S A CHANCE AHEAD!

RIGHT! HOLD TIGHT!

What was Nasti's game? He gave an evil snigger as he deliberately sheared off the tip of a spiky hillock.

SNIGGER! NOW THEY'LL REALLY HAVE A FIGHT ON THEIR HANDS, NASTI!

WHAT A PITY WE CAN'T STAY TO WATCH THE FUN, BADSER!

WHAT DID THEY DO THAT FOR, JACK?

OOH! LOOK OUT, CURLY!

The moment Jack and Curly took to the air again, the avenging Stingers swarmed into the attack. But this time the boys were ready for them.

What a battle! Like knights of old on their chargers, Jack and Curly fought a rearguard action against the deadly horde. Curly was glad of his leathery shield. Time and again it saved him. And he slashed and thrust with his thorn lance while Jack sprayed the sky with blasts from his M-glove.

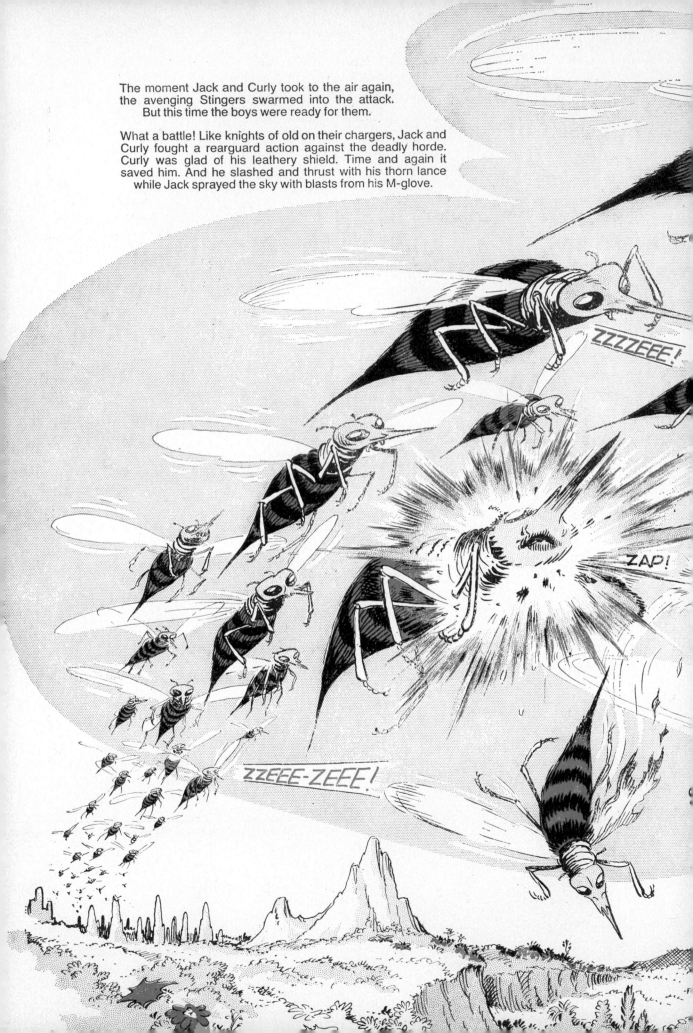

The sweet smell of the honey was far stronger than that of the flowers. Now instead of slowing right down, the hungry Buzzers put on a spurt.

WE'LL CATCH THEM NOW, CURLY!

I'M GOING AS FAST AS I CAN, BADSER!

BUZZ!

WHOA!

QUICK, CURLY! HELP ME SAVE THE SCOOTER!

BUZZ!

WAH!

YAIEEE!

Jack's plan worked almost too well! The Buzzers made such a pell mell charge that they collided with the scooter and knocked the thieves off it.

Jack and Curly just managed to grab the scooter and hold on. Lucky for them that they did, for now the Buzzers were diving after the thieves.

GASP! WE JUST MADE IT.

Then — Whump! — The two rogues thumped down on to a patch of thick-leaved bushes — and they bounced! The leaves were rubbery!

WHAT A PITY THAT COULDN'T HAVE BEEN A DUCK POND!

OOF!

ULK!

Nasti and Badser shrieked as they plummetted downwards. It looked as if their days of thieving and troublemaking were to be ended.

BUZZ-UM!

BUZZ-UM!

HELP!

H-H-HELP

The wind had been knocked right out of Nasti and Badser, and The Buzzers alighted on them and began sucking the honey.

It had been an exciting day for Jack and Curly and the boys were pleased as punch at recapturing their scooter. But as far as Curly was concerned, the best part of the day came later at the honey farm, when he settled down to a feast of bread and honey. Yummy!

CORPORAL CLOTT

COLONEL GRUMBLY SENT ME TO GET HIM A HORSE-SHOE.

BLACKSMITH

BAH! THAT JACKDAW HAS PINCHED A SMALL PACKAGE FROM ME, CLOTT!

DON'T WORRY, SOLDIER! I'LL GET IT BACK FOR YOU!

CRUMBS! I'VE MISSED, AND THE PEBBLE'S GONE THROUGH THE COLONEL'S WINDOW!

YOU'VE MADE THE JACKDAW DROP THE PACKAGE THOUGH, CLOTT.

CLONK!

RUN, BEFORE THE COLONEL SPOTS US!

A LITTLE LATER—
HERE'S YOUR HORSESHOE, SIR!

OH, GOOD! I'LL HANG IT ABOVE MY DOOR!

THAT'S THE PLACE FOR IT . . .

HERE'S YOUR PACKAGE, SIR.

AH, YES! IT'S MY WATCH WHICH WAS AWAY FOR REPAIR.

I'LL JUST OPEN IT AND— EEK! IT'S ALL IN BITS AND PIECES!

PING!

OOYAH!

GROAN!

WHAT DID THE COLONEL WANT THE HORSESHOE FOR ANYWAY?

HE WANTED IT TO BRING HIM *GOOD LUCK!*

COME BACK, YOU ROTTER. BAH! WE'LL NEVER CATCH HIM!

HEY! STOP, THIEF!

BYE-BYE FOR NOW, MUGS! I'LL SEE YOU AT THE CONTEST!

THAT SETTLES IT! WE'VE GOT TO STOP HIM WINNING AND I THINK I'VE GOT THE ANSWER!

PRESENTLY

HERE ARE LISTS OF THINGS I WANT YOU TO FETCH.

HARDWARE AND IRONMONGER A.W.

KORKY WANTS ME TO GO TO THE IRONMONGER'S SHOP.

I WONDER WHAT HE WANTS WITH A BUNDLE OF CANES AND A BAG OF SIX-INCH NAILS?

HARDWARE

NAILS

I HOPE THE BAKER'S GOT WHAT KORKY NEEDS!

BAKER & CONFECTIONER

BAKER AND CONFECTIONER

THAT WAS LUCKY! THE BAKER TURNED UP TRUMPS, BUT WHAT DOES KORKY WANT A TRAY OF BROKEN PIES FOR?

BAKER & CONFEC

JOE'S GARA

KORKY HAS SENT ME ALONG TO THE GARAGE WITH THIS LIST.

I CAN'T THINK WHAT HE WANTS A SET OF SPRINGS FOR?

BACK AT KORKY'S HOUSE

WELL DONE, LADS! BRING EVERYTHING IN, AND WE'LL GET TO WORK!

GET TO WORK ON WHAT?

LISTEN CAREFULLY, LADS! THIS IS WHAT WE'RE GOING TO DO—

AND SO—AT THE FANCY DRESS CONTEST

HEE-HEE! I'M SURE OF A PRIZE!

AND NOW, LADIES AND GENTLEMEN —A SPECIAL ENTRY REPRESENTING KORKY'S ZOO!

GRAND FANCY DRESS COMPETITION

TURN OVER TWO PAGES FOR CONTINUATION

PUMPKIN

ATTITUDE

MISCHIEF

WHEREFORE?

HERMIT

SPOKESMAN

PAGES FROM WINKER WATSON'S

GRUESOME

DANDELION

ACROBAT

NATIONALISE

PEN PALS

JARGON

BOBBYSOX

PELICAN

FIRE ESCAPE

NOTWITHSTANDING

KINKY

SNIP-SNIP-SNIP!

JUST A TRIM, PLEASE!

SAILING CLIPPER

Z-Z-Z-Z-Z!

KIDNAP

FOR SALE

BARGAIN

GOING CHEAP

ANY OFFERS?

DIGEM AND FLOGEM

AUCTIONEERS

WHOLESALE

TY

URE

X

PHEW!

HUMBUG

ABUNDANCE

HAVE A LAUGH AT THE FUNNY NEW MEANINGS WINKER HAS GIVEN TO SOME COMMON WORDS

PEEK A BOO.

COWHIDE

THAT'S MY BOY!

TREASON

BLACKMAIL

PERMISSION TO LAND?

HIPPODROME

SNORE!

INTENT

OO-ER! I FEEL ILL!

TICK! TICK! TICK! TICK!

TOXIC

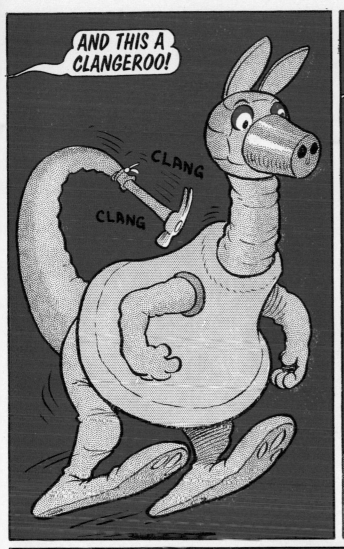

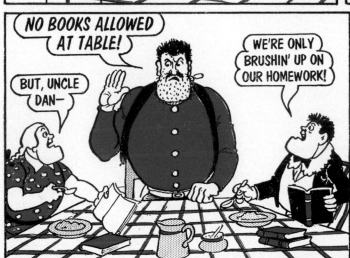

ROBIN HOOD'S SCHOOLDAYS

Alas, the feed was interrupted. The sound of approaching footsteps alerted Tim Trott.

WATCH IT— HERE COMES CREEPY!

Mr Creep was the Third Form Master. But Winker reckoned he knew how to fool him.

QUICK, LADS, HIDE, WHILE I OPEN THE WINDOW!

Creepy was very short sighted. He blinked around without seeing any of the hidden boys. But when he saw that open window, he at once jumped to the wrong conclusion.

I KNOW I HEARD SOME BOYS IN HERE—I BET THEY'VE CLIMBED OUT OF THE WINDOW!

While Creepy peered around outside the window, Winker and Company were making a bee-line for the door behind his back.

SLAM!

CLICK!

OH, NO! I'VE BEEN TRICKED! THEY WERE HERE ALL THE TIME, AND NOW THEY'VE GONE AND LOCKED ME IN!

There was nothing Creepy could do now, but holler. And how he hollered! Winker crept through the bushes towards him, planning another trick.

HELP! I'M LOCKED IN THE STORE ROOM! SOMEBODY, HELP!

GOLLY, CREEPY ISN'T HALF KICKING UP A ROW! PERHAPS A JAM TART WILL KEEP HIM QUIET!

HELP... OOF!

SPLAT!

Bull's-eye! As well as being a champion wangler, Winker was a catapult crackshot.

It wasn't long before Creepy's cries alerted the Headmaster. But there was nothing he could do except call for outside help.

HURRY NEXT DOOR TO THE POLICE COLLEGE, WATSON, AND ASK THE SUPERINTENDENT TO COME WITH HIS BUNCH OF SKELETON KEYS.

YESSIR, HEADMASTER, SIR!

The Superintendent of the Police College next door to Greytowers came round himself. And Creepy's jammy face made everyone think it was he who'd had a secret feast.

REALLY, MR CREEP! YOU SHOULD KNOW BETTER!

Meanwhile, those keys of the Superintendent's that could open any door gave Winker a corker of an idea. He dashed off to see some students he knew.

HO-HO! SURE WE'LL HELP, YOUNG WATSON. WAIT HERE WHILE WE MAKE IT UP INTO PARCELS.

MEDICAL SCHOOL STUDENTS ENTRANCE

The students were as good as their word. Winker and his pals were soon laden with some very queer-shaped parcels.

GOLLY, THANKS! WE'LL TAKE GREAT CARE OF EVERY BIT.

At Greytowers, Mr Creep was suspicious of those parcels. But he could put two and two together!

NOW THE ONLY REASON THOSE DOGS ARE FOLLOWING THE BOYS MUST BE BECAUSE THOSE PARCELS CONTAIN FOOD!

HEY! YOU, BOY, AT THE END THERE . . .

Creepy strode forward and grabbed the parcel. And in doing so he put Winker's whole plan in jeopardy.

I'M CONFISCATING THAT PARCEL OF YOURS! HAND IT OVER AND DON'T ARGUE!

What happened next convinced Creepy that he was right about what was in the parcel. As it happened, he really was right — well, half right!

The Master was so intent upon watching the dogs behind him, that he didn't notice what was in front. And that was a painful mistake!

Creepy had no chance to spot the culprit, for one of the dogs pounced, and made off with the parcel.

Those chaps were rugger players, but even their flying tackles failed to stop the dog.

Creepy hadn't seen the parcel being dropped. Winker unwrapped it in Dorm Three. And inside was a bone! So Creepy had been right in suspecting smuggled food, though wrong in thinking it was for secret feasting.

Meanwhile, Creepy's yells alerted someone else. The Superintendent of the Cop College.

STOP THAT DOG!

THAT'S MR CREEP'S VOICE! MY WORD, HE ALWAYS SEEMS TO BE NEEDING MY HELP!

The Super took that spotted pooch into custody just as easily as you please— with the help of his big police jacket.

GOT YOU!

YELP!

The dog was caught, but as Creepy explained, the dog wasn't really what he was after. Neither man could see two pairs of schoolboy ears flapping nearby.

WELL DONE, SUPERINTENDENT, BUT THE BRUTE MUST HAVE DROPPED THE PARCEL IT STOLE. WILL YOU HELP ME SEARCH FOR IT?

IT'S OUR DUTY TO BE HELPFUL, MR CREEP.

HEAR THAT, WINKER? THE SUPER IS GOING TO HELP OLD CREEPY LOOK FOR THAT PARCEL.

OH, IS HE? RIGHT, THEN, WE'D BETTER MAKE SURE HE FINDS IT!

The Super hadn't been hunting long when he spotted a schoolboy behaving suspiciously.

OHO! HERE COMES THAT WATSON BOY, AND HE'S TRYING TO HIDE SOMETHING UNDER HIS COAT! VERY SUSPICIOUS, I MUST SAY ...

Winker was a born actor, and he looked really guilty when the policeman "surprised" him.

GOT YOU, BOY! AND MR CREEP'S MISSING PARCEL, I'LL BE BOUND!

OO-ER! YOU DIDN'T HALF MAKE ME JUMP, SUPERINTENDENT!

PLOP!

But Creepy got a big disappointment with the contents of the parcel. Perhaps he had been hoping to sink his teeth into some choice grub.

IT'S A BONE!

THAT'S RIGHT, MR CREEP, SIR. WE BOUGHT IT FOR MATRON'S DOG'S BIRTHDAY AND WE DIDN'T WANT THAT OTHER DOG TO GRAB IT FIRST!

There was more fun to come! Winker had set his pals to round up more dogs, and they were lots hungrier than the one which had pinched the other bone.

RIGHT, LADS! CREEPY'S GOT THE BONE UNWRAPPED—SO LET THE POOCHES LOOSE LIKE WINKER SAID.

SNIFF!

SNIFF!

I MUST GO NOW MR CREEP, SIR, OR I'LL BE LATE FOR CLASS!

SNIFF! GRR-R!

YELP!

SNARL!

And behind him Creepy and the Superintendent were bowled over in a whirl of snarling hounds.

Meanwhile, Winker's trickery had left yet another person in the school really puzzled!

THAT'S FUNNY! I CAN'T FIND THAT BIG BONE I WAS BOILING UP FOR TOMORROW'S SOUP! SURELY IT CAN'T HAVE BOILED AWAY TO NOTHING?

SCHOOL KITCHEN

Creepy and the Super were struggling to gather their wits. Now they found that more than one thing was missing!

OH, DEAR, THEY'VE STOLEN THE BONE! ER—THANK YOU FOR YOUR HELP, SUPERINTENDENT. I MUST GO NOW. THE THIRD FORM IS WAITING FOR ME.

I DON'T CARE ABOUT THE SILLY BONE, MR CREEP, BUT ONE OF THOSE BEASTS MADE OFF WITH MY BEST CAP!

Creepy reached the classroom just in time to see Winker passing a note to Tim Trott. He didn't know it, but Winker meant him to see that!

PSST! CATCH HOLD OF THIS, TIM!

THANKS, WINKER!

STOP WHATEVER YOU'RE DOING, WATSON, AND PAY ATTENTION! SIT UP, BOYS, AND GET OUT YOUR GEOGRAPHY BOOKS.

After class, Creepy went snooping—and made a find. It was the bait that was to lure him into Winker's next trap!

AH, TROTT HAS LEFT THAT NOTE WATSON GAVE HIM ON HIS DESK. LET'S SEE WHAT IT SAYS...ER, "MEET IN CUPBOARD UNDER STAIRS AT 4.30."

Another secret feast! Creepy felt sure about that. So he rang up the **Super** once more.

LEND ME YOUR SKELETON KEYS, SUPERINTENDENT, AND I'LL OPEN THE DOOR AND CATCH THEM REDHANDED!

What a fright for Creepy and the Super. The skeleton keys revealed a skeleton in the cupboard! It was this that Winker had borrowed from those medical students.

EEEK!

When their hearts stopped fluttering, the two men pressed bravely on with their quest for the secret feasters.

IT'S ONLY A SILLY PRACTICAL JOKE, MR CREEP, BUT WE'D BETTER GO IN AND CHECK UP.

OO-ER! YOU LEAD THE WAY, SUPER!

And now Winker made sure the nosey parkers got what they deserved! And at the same time he got what he specially wanted!

HEE-HEE! GOT 'EM! AND WHAT'S MORE—I'VE GOT THE BUNCH OF SKELETON KEYS, TOO!

SLAM! CLICK!

That bunch of keys could let Winker into a whole lot of Aladdin's Caves! No more bread and butter meals for the Third Form!

LOOK, LADS! WITH THIS LITTLE LOT WE CAN UNLOCK THE DOORS TO EVERY PANTRY, STORE CUPBOARD AND KITCHEN IN THE SCHOOL HERE AND IN THE POLICE COLLEGE NEXT DOOR!

COME ON THEN, WINKER, WHAT'S STOPPING US?— LET'S GO!

What a spree! The Third Formers had never had a dormitory feast like this in their lives, and all thanks to the wangles of the super wangler, Winker Watson!

GET CRACKING, LADS, FOR THE BLOW-OUT OF THE CENTURY, AND LET'S START WITH A TOAST TO THE MAN WHO INVENTED SKELETON KEYS!

POLICE CANTEEN

MR CREEP PRIVATE

CRISPS

LOVE FROM AUNTY

POP

I'LL SOON OPEN THAT DOOR WITH THESE, HEADMASTER!

OH, NO, YOU WON'T, CONSTABLE! IF I CAN'T UNLOCK THE DOOR WITH A PIECE OF BENT WIRE, THEY'LL STAY IN THERE UNTIL YOU FIND YOUR SKELETON KEYS!

OPEN THIS DOOR AT ONCE!

EEEK! OO-ER! IT'S DARK IN HERE, HEADMASTER, SIR! HURRY UP AND GET US OUT!

The Head wasn't much good at picking locks, and he didn't want any damage done, so wouldn't allow anyone to break the door open. Upstairs, the feasters could feast in peace.

CLAUDE HOPPER

OH, NO! MY PAINTING WILL BE RUINED!

YIPPEE! THIS UMBRELLA HAS COME IN USEFUL ALL RIGHT!

WHAT CAN I DO TO SAVE MY PICTURE?

I KNOW!

HOW'S THAT?

AFTER THE RAIN—

TELL YOU WHAT, KORKY. I'LL SWAP A BOX OF PAINTS FOR YOUR UMBRELLA IN CASE IT RAINS AGAIN.

IT'S A DEAL!

SMASHING! I'LL GO HOME AND DO SOME PAINTING!

JUST ROUND THE CORNER—

IT'S AGAINST THE LAW! YOU CAN'T DRIVE YOUR VAN WITHOUT A NUMBER PLATE!

IT MUST HAVE DROPPED OFF, CONSTABLE!

FRESH FISH DAILY

I DON'T KNOW WHAT I'M GOING TO DO, KORKY— I'VE GOT A LOAD OF FISH TO DELIVER.

LEAVE IT TO ME!

DAIL

102 D

THAT'S GREAT, KORKY!

THANKS, KORKY! NOW HERE'S SOMETHING FOR YOU!

FRESH FISH ILY

LATER—

HELLO, MR PERKINS! HOW MANY DID YOU CATCH THEN?

ER, I DIDN'T CATCH ANY!

WELL, I DID— *LOOK!*

GASP! I DON'T BELIEVE IT!

What game do horses like playing best?—Stable tennis!

LET ME SEE NOW. FIRST OF ALL THERE WAS ...

DICK THE DIRTY SAXON, WHO OPENED KING ALFRED'S OVEN AND DISCOVERED THAT THE KING HAD BURNT THE CAKES.

DICK THE NAVIGATOR, WHO LANDED IN AMERICA WITH COLUMBUS. HE WAS THE MAN WHO GAVE THE RED INDIANS THE IDEA OF USING WAR PAINT.

THAT'S UM HEAP GOOD IDEA. UM PALEFACE HAS PAINTED HIMSELF AND HE DOESN'T HALF LOOK FIERCE

WAIT TILL I FIND THE MAN WHO DROPPED THIS PAINT POT ON ME. I'LL HALF KILL HIM

GREAT UNCLE DICK, THE NAVVY. THE ONLY MAN TO STRIKE OIL IN OUR TOWN. THE SILLY CLOT BURST AN OIL PIPE!

OOPS!

GREAT-GREAT-GRANDFATHER DICK, THE CHEF WHO INVENTED SCRAMBLED EGGS.

THAT CAT TRIPPED ME! I'LL JUST HAVE TO SCRAPE UP ALL THIS EGG AND MAKE A DISH OF IT!

EGGS

PRIVATE DICK, THE SOLDIER WHO INVENTED CAMOUFLAGE.

DONNER UND BLITZEN! DER BRITISHER CAME THIS WAY, BUT HE HAS DISAPPEARED!

PIG STY

GOOD JOB I'M BRITAIN'S DIRTIEST SOLDIER. I CAN EAT MY CHOCOLATE CAKE IN PEACE!

PROFESSOR DICK, THE MAN WHO ALMOST INVENTED A VACUUM CLEANER THAT WORKED.

DIRTY DICK TURPIN AND HIS HORSE BLACK BESS. HAW-HAW! IT'S EASY TO SEE HOW THEY GOT THEIR NAMES!

SPLASH!

HEE-HEE! GOOD OLD GRANDPA! HE'S AN AWFUL FIBBER, BUT HE DOESN'T HALF KNOW HOW TO PUT DAD IN HIS PLACE!

ROBIN HOOD'S SCHOOLDAYS

WE'VE SAVED ALL THESE GROATS TO BUY THE BIGGEST BIRTHDAY CAKE EVER, FOR IT'S LITTLE JOHN'S BIRTHDAY TODAY.

SLURP!

HERE YOU ARE, ROBIN HOOD. I'VE PUT EXTRA CREAM ON THIS ONE!

LOVELY! DON'T BOTHER TO WRAP IT UP. WE'LL TAKE IT AS IT IS!

UT, OUTSIDE—

A BIRTHDAY CAKE! WHY, THANK YOU!

WOW! THE SHERIFF OF NOTTINGHAM!

IT'S MY BIRTHDAY TODAY—AND THIS IS MY TENTH CAKE. I'M HAVING A PARTY TONIGHT.

IF HE WANTS OUR CAKE, HE CAN HAVE IT —BUT HE WON'T ENJOY IT!

YEEOW! WHAT'S GOING ON?

TRIP!

THUD!

THAT'S OUR CAKE RUINED. NOW WE'LL HAVE TO TRY TO GET A SHARE OF THE SHERIFF'S CAKES!

OOF!

SPLAT!

LATER—

HELLO, TEACHER! WE CAN'T STOP 'COS THERE BE A MAGICIAN IN THE FOREST, AND SINCE IT'S LITTLE JOHN'S BIRTHDAY, HE'S GOING TO TURN ALL THIS METAL INTO GOLD!

A MAGICIAN? GOLD? I MUST TELL THE SHERIFF!

DESPERATE DAN

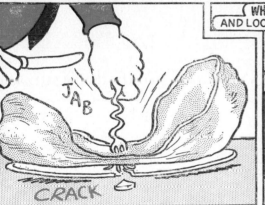

MYSTERIES

CAN YOU SOLVE THEM? CAN YOU GUESS WHAT WINKER IS UP TO IN EACH OF THESE PICTURES?... YOU'LL FIND THE 12 FUNNY ANSWERS ON THE NEXT PAGE.

ANSWERS TO THE
12 WINKER WATSON MYSTERIES (SEE PREVIOUS PAGE)

1. Returning a book to the school library.
2. Watching Mr Creep lose the toss.
3. Training for the hundred yards dash.
4. Helping Creepy to stop smoking.
5. Wondering what to buy Mr Creep for his birthday.
6. Exercising Matron's dog.
7. Getting rid of weeds in Matron's garden.
8. Coming out top of the class.
9. Giving Mr Creep an eye-sight test. (He failed!)
10. Winning the egg-and-spoon race.
11. Brewing hot tea for Creepy.
12. Making a six-hit.

BRASSNECK

CHARLEY BRAND held his breath, then let out a yell of delight as his amazing metal pal Brassneck pulled off one of the most fantastic tricks ever seen in a circus ring. Brassneck was a mechanical marvel, his innards chock full of electric works.

But what were Brassneck and Charley doing in a circus ring? And why was Charley's Dad togged up in a Ringmaster's costume? For the answer to these questions, and a trunk-load of Jumbo-sized laughs, turn the page and read on . . .

One day, when all was quiet in Charley Brand's house, a visitor arrived.

I'M BORED! I WISH SOMETHING EXCITING WOULD HAPPEN.

THERE'S SOMEONE WITH A BRIEFCASE COMING UP THE PATH, DAD.

This wasn't the kind of excitement Dad was looking for. He rapped out an order and scuttled from the room.

GASP! I BET HE'S A ROTTEN BILL COLLECTOR. GET RID OF HIM, CHARLEY.

B-BUT— HOW?

Charley was in a fluster, but Brassneck was already rushing upstairs with a plan in mind.

G-GOSH! WHAT'LL I SAY, BRASSNECK?

HOLD ON! I KNOW WHAT TO DO.

KNOCK! KNOCK!

Just as well Charley's Mum was out! She'd have flattened the rascal if she'd caught him togged out in her Grandma's finery.

YES, SIR. THIS IS THE GLADYS SLINGEM HOME FOR RETIRED LADY WRESTLERS. CAN I HELP YOU?

OOH! I MUST HAVE THE WRONG ADDRESS.

The ruse worked a treat—but Brassneck's ears popped as he heard what the man had to say.

MY NAME'S STAMPIT, AND I'M A LAWYER. I WAS LOOKING FOR A MR BRAND—ABOUT AN INHERITANCE HE'S COME INTO . . .

WHAT?

Dad Brand's ears were popping, too, and he came scampering out of hiding, yelling like a kid.

HERE I AM! HOW MUCH DO I GET?

HOLD ON!

Dad was looking for money, and he was disappointed. But Charley whooped. This inheritance was more exciting than cash.

IT APPEARS, MR BRAND, THAT YOUR GREAT UNCLE BEN HAS LEFT YOU A CIRCUS.

TERRIFIC!

WHAT D'YOU MEAN, TERRIFIC? I DON'T WANT A CIRCUS!

Unable to contain their excitement, Charley and Brassneck got Dad to drive straight over to visit the circus.

AW, GEE, DAD! THIS IS MORE LIKE A GIPSY CAMP THAN A CIRCUS!

TOWN TIP

Charley was right with a vengeance — the circus was tattier than a pair of old boots. And a run of accidents had left the ringmaster with hardly any acts to put on. No wonder folk weren't flocking to see the show any more.

THE ROPE SNAPPED DURING MY ACT.

IF YOU'RE THE NEW OWNER, HOW ABOUT LENDING ME A QUID?

WHAT'S FUNNY? THERE'S NOTHING TO LAUGH AT AROUND HERE.

Dad grew more and more disheartened. For the more he saw, the more he reckoned he'd inherited the circus just in time to see it go bust.

THAT'S THE GREAT MARIO. HE WAS OUR LAST GOOD ACT, UNTIL SOMEONE PUT ANTS IN HIS PANTS UP ON THE TIGHT ROPE!

But Charley had been thinking. And he wasn't willing to give up the new family business without a fight.

HEY, DAD! WHY DON'T WE PUT ON A SHOW OURSELVES? BRASSNECK CAN DO LOTS OF CLEVER TRICKS, AND YOU COULD BE THE RINGMASTER!

YEAH!

WHO? ME? WELL, I SUPPOSE WE CAN ONLY TRY.

Charley and Brassneck put up posters advertising the new circus star. And that evening a new Ringmaster strutted around welcoming the throng.

FIX HIM, HERNANDO, LIKE YOU FIXED THE OTHERS!

But not everyone was pleased with this turn of events. In fact, Buffalo Bill Bloggs, the owner of another circus, was raging — and having a secret talk with Hernando, the trapeze artist.

ROLL UP! ROLL UP!

As the lights came on in the Big Top, the tubby Ringmaster stepped forward to announce the first act.

INTRODUCING TO YOU, FOR THE FIRST TIME, FOLKS — THE MASKED JUGGLER!

It was Brassneck. He wore a hood — and instead of juggling with clubs, he juggled with chairs!

FANTASTIC!

AMAZING!

But there was trickery afoot. Hernando seized the end of the carpet on which Brassneck stood, and suddenly heaved.

THAT METAL MARVEL IS TOO GOOD FOR THIS CIRCUS!

Kerrash! Clatter! Whump! Brassneck's feet were tugged from under him, and an instant later he was half buried under the chairs.

W-WOW! BRASSNECK! WHAT HAPPENED?

WHUMP!

CRASH!

CLATTER!

BANG!

Dad was lost for words. So while Brassneck was being rescued, he entertained with a song.

OH-NELL-EE-DEAN!

GASP! I THOUGHT IT WAS ONLY THE JUGGLER WHO WAS HURT!

GET OFF!

The audience didn't like Dad's singing! Fortunately the next act was ready quickly. It was a tomahawk thrower.

ER—THANK YOU, FOLKS! HERE'S THE NEXT ACT— BIG CHIEF BRASSNECK!

HOW, FOLKS!

GULP! ARE YOU SURE YOU NEED ME, BRASSNECK?

Every eye was on the hawk-eyed Redskin Chief as he landed the tomahawks inches away from Charley's trembling arms and legs. Dad Brand was too scared to look, but he glimpsed something which horrified him.

GASP!

AMAZING!

SNIGGER!

HEY! WHAT'S GOING ON OVER THERE?

DON'T PANIC, ANYBODY.

In an instant Brassneck's whole headdress was ablaze. As flames shot up, there was only one thing for it.

Brassneck was out of luck! The tub wasn't full of water, but custard for the clown to throw.

HEY! WHAT ARE YOU DOING IN MY CUSTARD?

WATCH IT, MATE, OR I'LL SCALP YOU!

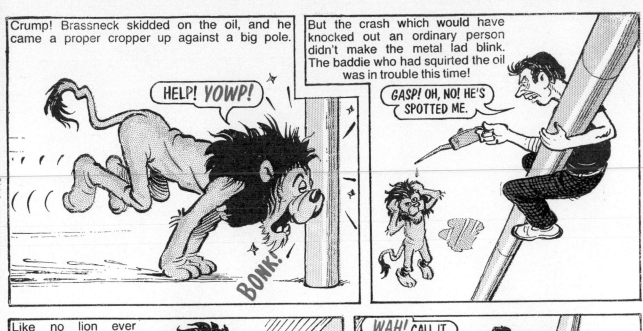

Hernando landed from his trapeze on the platform he had been aiming for, and started shinning higher up the huge tent pole.

GASP! HE'S STILL AFTER ME!

NOW TO KNOCK SPOTS OFF THAT CROOK!

The twister had one last trick up his sleeve — the oil can in his pocket. A squirt from that would stop Brassneck from following.

TAKE THAT!

THE ROTTER!

SLOSH!

Sure enough, no matter how hard Brassneck tried to grip, he couldn't stop slithering downwards.

I'M SAFE! SAFE!

OH, NO, YOU'RE NOT!

But Brassneck had a trick up HIS sleeve. The metal marvel stretched his telescopic neck and snapped the lion's jaws over Hernando's rear end.

EEYOW!

SNAP!

Yahoo! The two-timing trapeze man shot skywards in pain, and his leap sent him bursting right out through the canvas roof!

YEEEAARGH!

Hernando came down with a thump on the back of his neck on the tightly stretched canvas of the roof.

OOF!

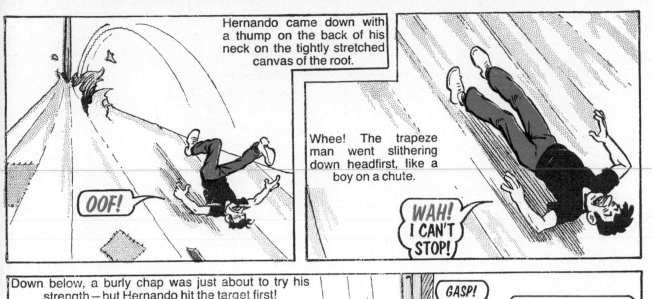

Whee! The trapeze man went slithering down headfirst, like a boy on a chute.

WAH! I CAN'T STOP!

Down below, a burly chap was just about to try his strength — but Hernando hit the target first!

YOW!

WOW!

YAHOO!

DONK!

GASP!

HEY! THAT MAN USED HIS HEAD INSTEAD OF THE HAMMER!

Whoosh! The indicator rocketed up the scale with such force that it knocked the bell off the top.

WHEEEE!

CRASH!

Buffalo Bill Bloggs was feeling very pleased with himself. He wasn't to know his henchman had dropped a clanger.

SNIGGER! MINE WILL BE THE ONLY CIRCUS LEFT WHEN THIS OLD HEAP CLOSES DOWN. I'LL MAKE A FORTUNE.

But next moment Buffalo Bill had a ringing in his ears! And it served him right, too, for all his nasty trickery.

DONG!

ULK!

Buffalo Bill and his henchman, Hernando, left town straight away after that. They couldn't bear to watch the crowds who had heard about Brassneck's fantastic acts rolling up and fighting to buy a seat.

WE WANT IN!

I'VE COME TEN MILES TO SEE THIS SHOW.

Among the crowd, however, was Mr Stampit, the lawyer, and he had bad news for Dad.

ER, I'M SORRY, THERE'S BEEN A MISTAKE, MR BRAND, A TYPING ERROR. IT'S MR BLAND HERE WHO HAS INHERITED THE CIRCUS, NOT YOU.

GULP!

WHAT A SHAME!

Charley and Brassneck were disgusted, and poor Dad, who had begun to enjoy his new job as Ringmaster, felt badly let down. The circus folk were so pleased with all that the Brands had done to save their circus, however, that they made Dad honorary Ringmaster and presented him with a full costume as his very own.

WE'D NEVER HAVE FOUND OUT ABOUT BLOGGS AND HERNANDO IF IT HADN'T BEEN FOR YOU AND YOUR LADS, MR BRAND. YOU'RE ALL WELCOME HERE ANYTIME.

THREE CHEERS, EVERYBODY!

HO-HO! WE'LL BE HERE EVERY WEEK!

So that's why if you ever take a stroll past Charley Brand's house, you're likely to see a Ringmaster in full costume conducting the world's smallest circus. But don't scoff, for Brassneck is the star, so you'll be seeing one of the world's most amazing circus acts!

ROLL UP! ROLL UP, FOLKS! I USED TO WORK IN THE CIRCUS, Y'KNOW.

LOWERING THE TONE OF THE NEIGHBOURHOOD, THIS IS!

HAW-HAW!

COME ON, FIDO! YOU CAN DO BETTER THAN THAT!

TIGHT-ROPE WALKING! COME DOWN, BRASSNECK! YOU'RE TRAMPLING ALL OVER MY WASHING!

WHUMP!

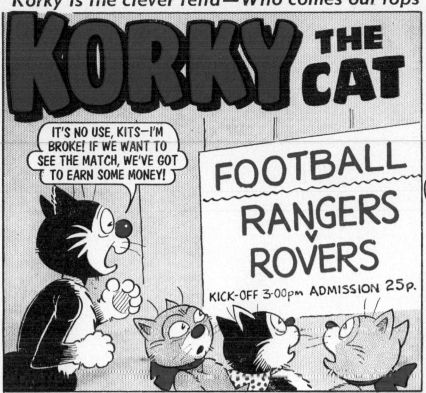

DESPERATE DAN!

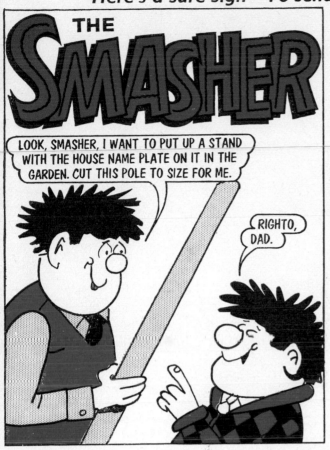